SAM & FUZZY

FIX YOUR PROBLEM

SAM LOGAN

Logo design by Brian Carroll and Sam Logan

Published by **Blind Ferret Entertainment, Inc**

2308 32nd Avenue

Montreal, QC

Canada

H8T 3H4

Originally serialized online at www.samandfuzzy.com between January 2009 and March 2010

www.samandfuzzy.com

www.topatoco.com

First Blind Ferret Edition April 2016

ISBN: 978-1-926838-37-3

10 9 8 7 6 5 4 3 2 1

Printed in China

TABLE OF CONTENTS

1
FRAME OF MIND

TEN YEARS LATER

OK,
DEV.

WHICH LOOKS MORE
EMPLOYABLE...

RED
BROOCH?

OR **BLUE**
BROOCH?

RED IS BOLD.
STRONG.

CONFIDENT.

ASSERTIVE!

BUT **BLUE**...
BLUE IS **COOL.**
SUBDUED.
RELAXED.

...MAYBE **TOO**
RELAXED?

24

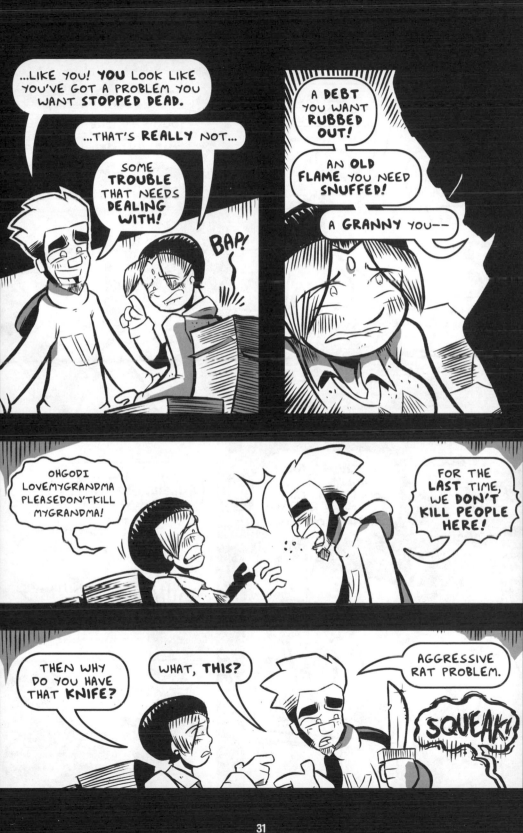

31

58

HUMAN PERCEPTIONS OF RODENTS!

HUMAN PERCEPTIONS OF RODENTS

THWACK!

GERBILS! COMPLETELY ADORABLE.

HAMSTERS! FLUFFY LITTLE SWEET-HEARTS.

SQUIRRELS! CUTE AND DELICIOUS.

BUT RATS?

DISGUSTING, UNIVERSALLY FEARED AND REVILED STREET VERMIN.

SO WHAT'S THE RAT'S SECRET?

WHAT DOES THIS NEARLY IDENTICAL RELATIVE HAVE THAT YOU ALL DON'T?

2
HAZEL

...THE HELL?

RED'S TAVERN, THURSDAY, 10:59 P.M.:

90

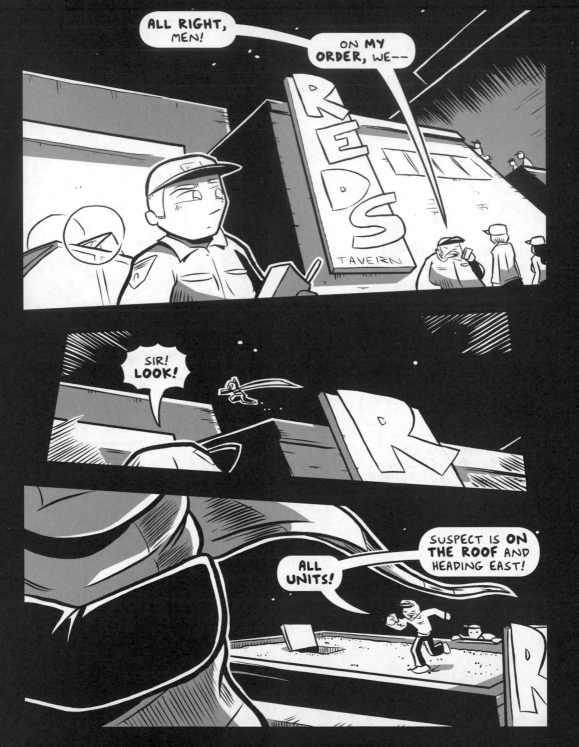

3
NINJA MAFIA
SERVICES

YOU'RE WATCHING **FACT COPY**...

...AMERICA'S MOST **TRUSTED JOURNALISTIC INSTITUTION.** (FOR MINDLESS CELEBRITY GOSSIP.)

TODAY: MUSIC SENSATION—

WHAM!

WE NEED TO TALK.

IT'S THESE **OLD JOB FILES** YOU'VE GOT ME SORTING.

I MEAN... **SOME** OF THEM... THEY **HAVE** TO BE JOKES, RIGHT?

LIKE WHAT?

118

124

4

THE BIG
CHEAT

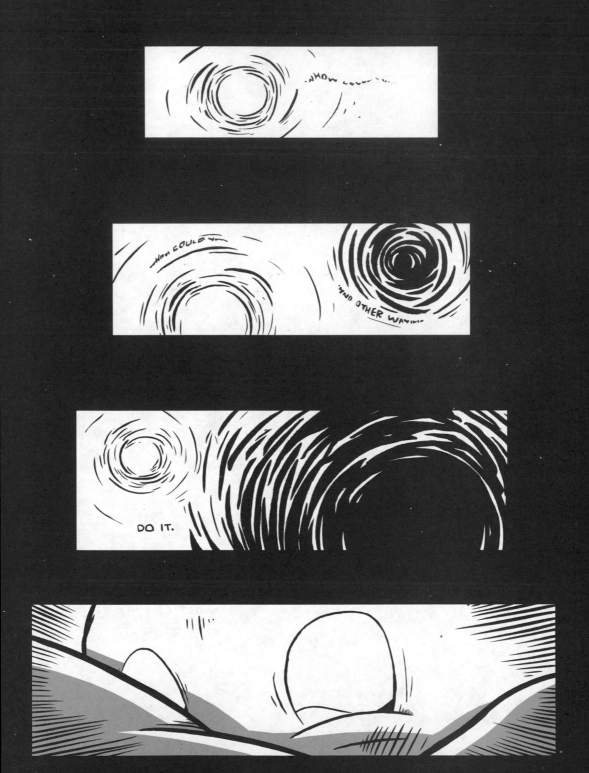

TEN YEARS AGO

130

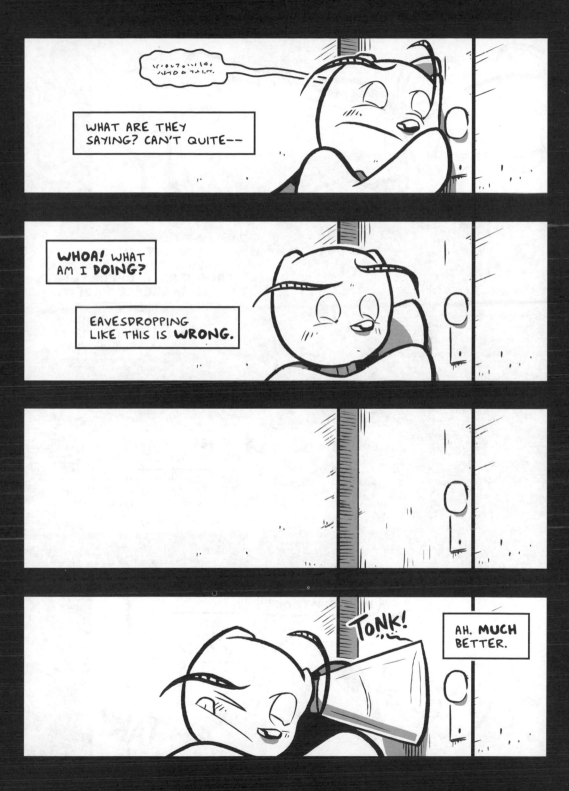

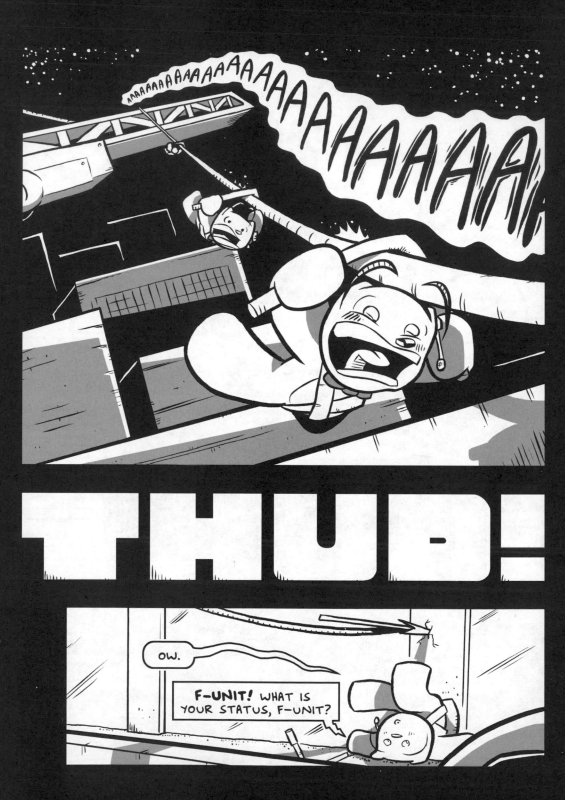

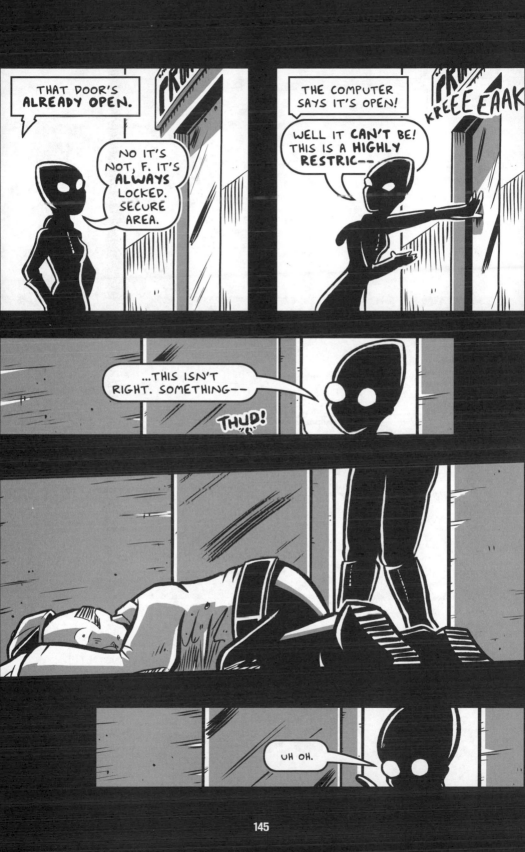

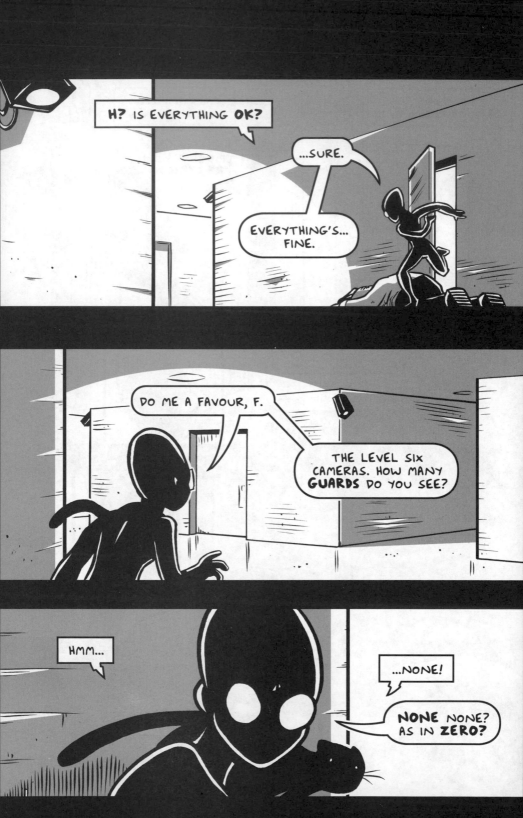

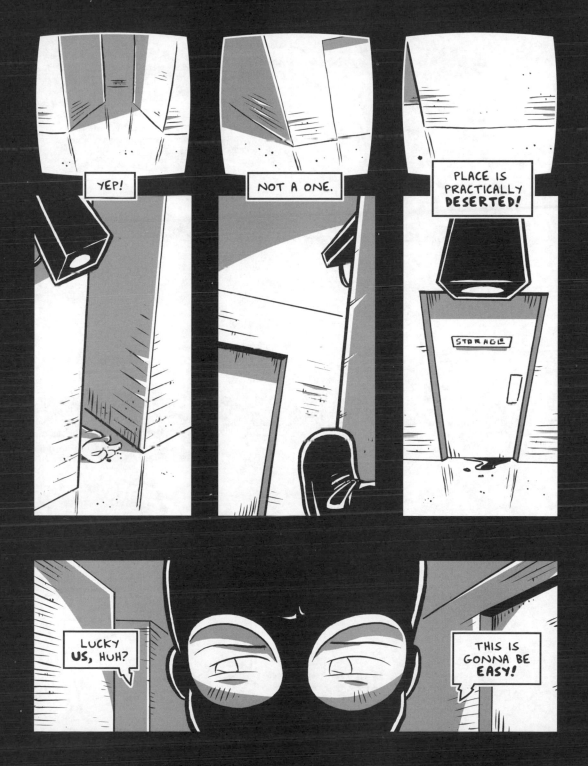

5
EDWIN

TEN YEARS LATER

173

174

175

187

202

214

6
BUYER BEWARE

AAAAAND WE'RE CLEAR.

SPITOO!

GUH!

DID YOU **HEAR** WHAT THAT LITTLE TROLLOP CALLED ME?!?

LET IT GO, DUMPY.

229

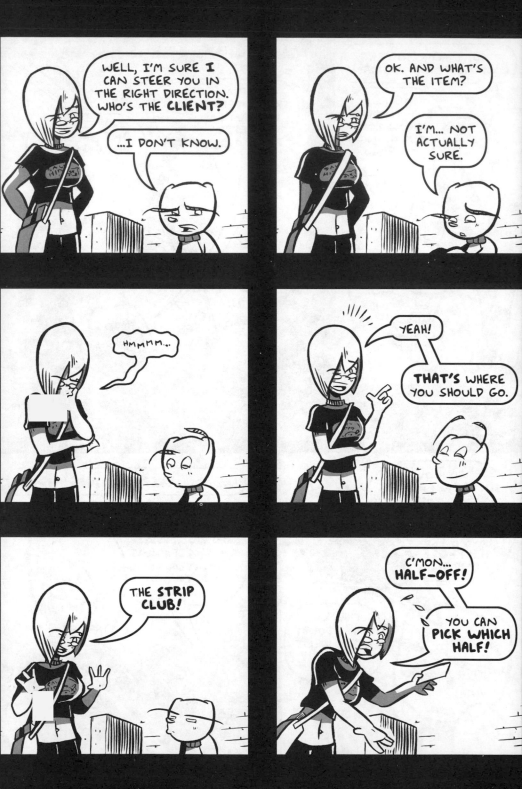

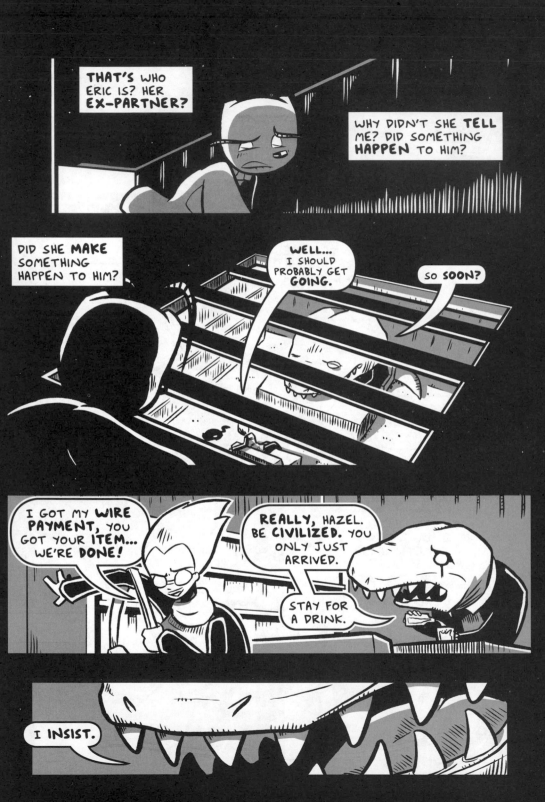

266

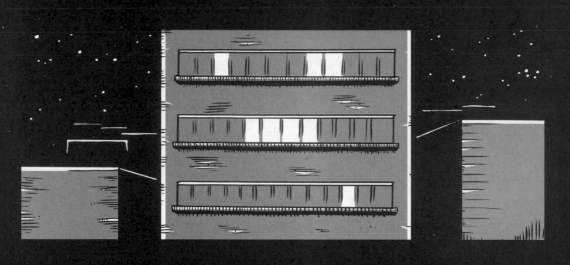

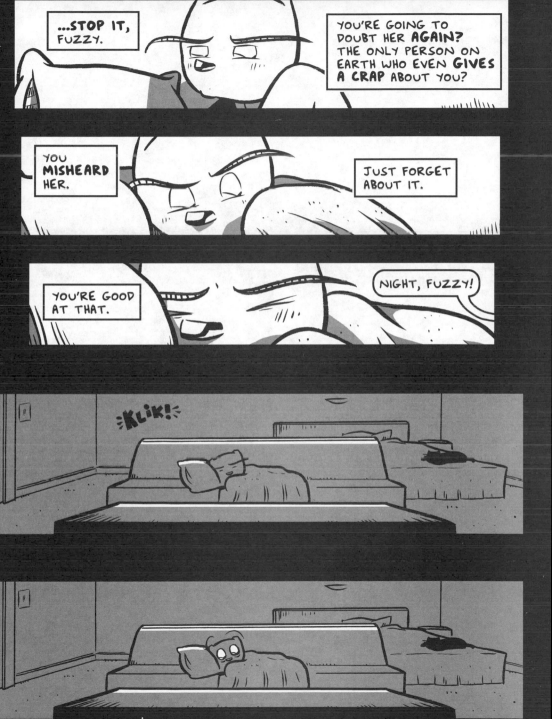

7

EMPLOYEE OF THE MONTH

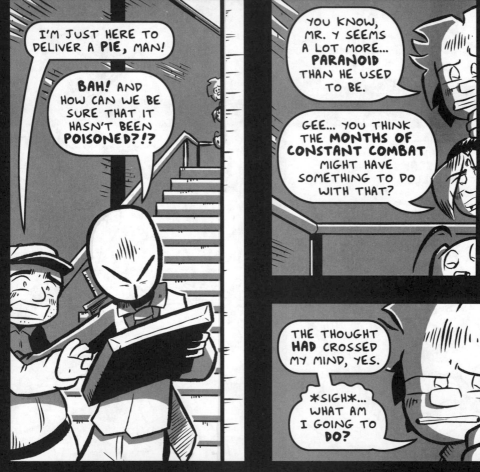

310

DAY TWENTY.

8

INHUMAN

10 YEARS AGO

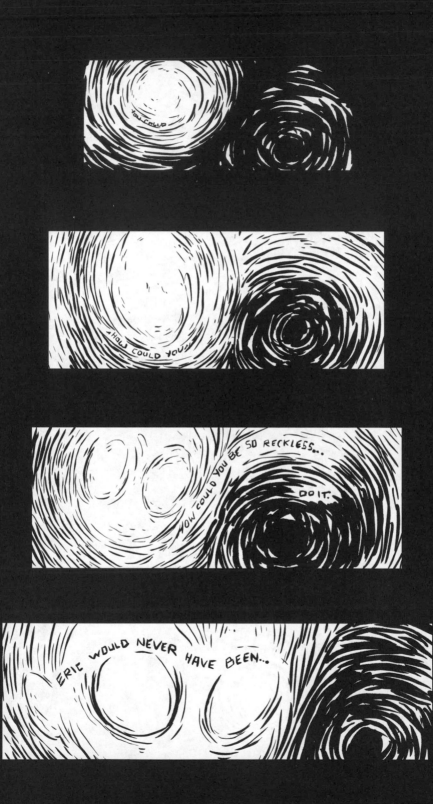

330

TRY TO **THINK** LIKE HER.

YOU'RE A DEJECTED CRIMINAL STUCK IN SOME GRIMY HOTEL IN THE MIDDLE OF NOWHERE.

WHERE WOULD **YOU** GO?

LAUNDRY
$2 PER LOAD ▸ $1

ICE
MACHINE

ALL NITE
BAR
AND
LOUNGE
NO MINORS

DAMN IT!

I CAN'T REMEMBER IF HAZEL LIKES ICE CUBES!

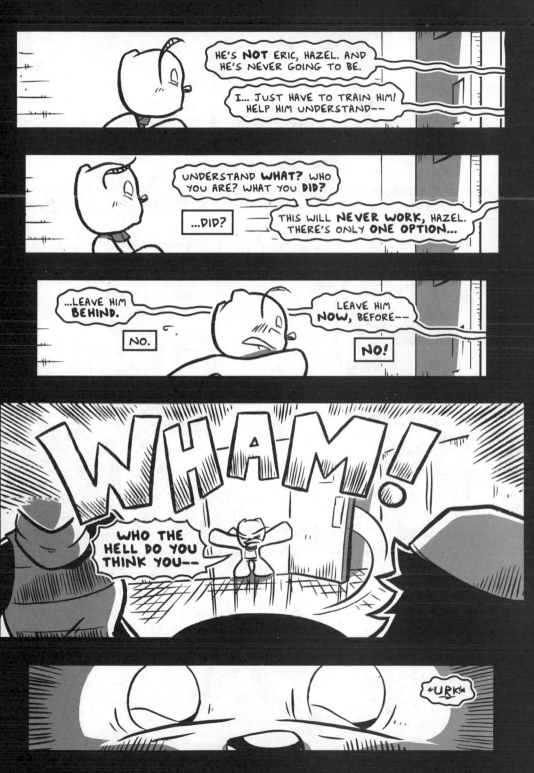

343

345

OK.

JUST GET THE MONEY.

SLAM!

Ziiiiiiiiiiiip!

STFF!

STFF!

346

TWO MONTHS LATER

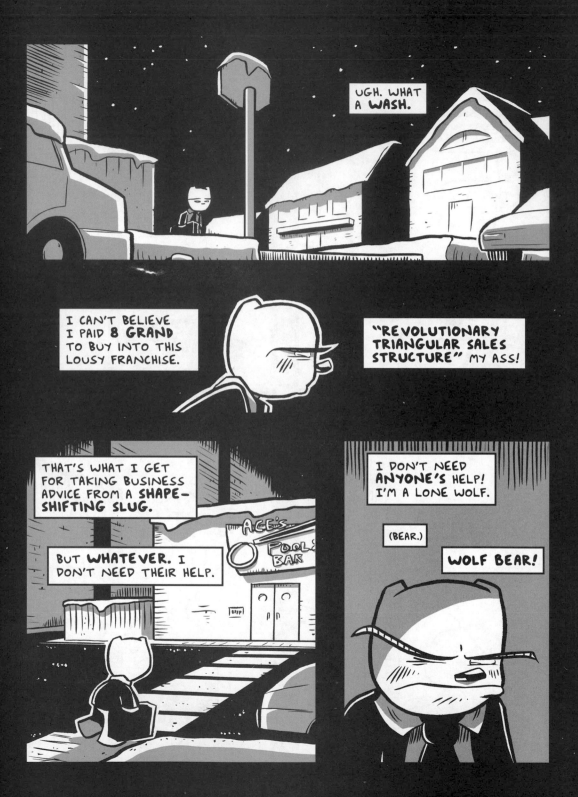

NEXT:
FAMOUS

ABOUT THE
AUTHOR

Sam (no relation) Logan is a 27-year-old artist living in Vancouver, BC. As a child, he drew thousands and thousands of pages of terrible comics.

ABOUT THE
COMIC

Sam and Fuzzy began as a strip in the University of Victoria's *Martlet* in 2001, and moved online shortly thereafter. Today, there are more than 1200 installments on the website, with an additional three premiering every week. Read them all at

www.samandfuzzy.com

HOW TO DRAW FUZZY in 10 EASY STEPS!

① DRAW TWO CIRCLES!

② ADD SOME TUBES FOR THE ARMS AND LEGS.

③ NEXT, DRAW AN EYELINE ACROSS THE HEAD TO HELP POSITION THE FACIAL FEATURES.

④ THEN DRAW EYELINES ON EVERYTHING ELSE, TOO.

⑤ USING A RULER, MEASURE THE DISTANCE FROM THE TOP TO THE BOTTOM AND DIVIDE BY SEVEN.

6 THEN, CALCULATE YOUR EXTERIOR DEPTHS USING A SIMPLE RIGHTWISE PERSPECTIVE TRIAD.

7 ON A SEPARATE PIECE OF PAPER, WRITE A SHORT ESSAY OUTLINING YOUR PROGRESS SO FAR AND YOUR HOPES FOR THE FUTURE.

8 DON'T FORGET TO TAKE ALL THE ART SUPPLIES YOU'VE USED AND BURN THEM IN A RITUAL SACRIFICE TO BLOTOVIA, GOD OF PEN AND INK.

9 FINALLY, JUST ADD A FEW MORE LINES...

10 ...AND YOU'RE DONE!

AND IT ONLY TOOK **FOUR HOURS!**

GOOD JOB, TEAM!

BUDDY SAVES CHRISTMAS!
THE GOLDFISH

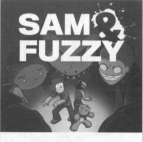